ANGRY BIRDS™

PIG 'N' MIX PUZZLE BOOK

PUFFIN

PUFFIN BOOKS

Published by the Penguin Group
Penguin Books Ltd, 80 Strand, London WC2R 0RL, England
Penguin Group (USA) Inc., 375 Hudson Street, New York, New York 10014, USA
Penguin Group (Canada), 90 Eglinton Avenue East, Suite 700, Toronto, Ontario,
Canada M4P 2Y3
(a division of Pearson Penguin Canada Inc.)
Penguin Ireland, 25 St Stephen's Green, Dublin 2, Ireland
(a division of Penguin Books Ltd)
Penguin Group (Australia), 707 Collins Street, Melbourne, Victoria 3008, Australia
(a division of Pearson Australia Group Pty Ltd)
Penguin Books India Pvt Ltd, 11 Community Centre, Panchsheel Park,
New Delhi – 110 017, India
Penguin Group (NZ), 67 Apollo Drive, Rosedale, Auckland 0632, New Zealand
(a division of Pearson New Zealand Ltd)
Penguin Books (South Africa) (Pty) Ltd, Block D, Rosebank Office Park,
181 Jan Smuts Avenue, Parktown North, Gauteng 2193, South Africa

Penguin Books Ltd, Registered Offices: 80 Strand, London WC2R 0RL, England

puffinbooks.com

First published 2013
001

Written by Stephanie Clarkson
Copyright © 2009–2013 Rovio Entertainment Ltd.
Rovio, Angry Birds, Bad Piggies, Mighty Eagle and all related titles, logos and
characters are trademarks of Rovio Entertainment Ltd.
All rights reserved.

Printed in Great Britain by Clays Ltd, St Ives plc

British Library Cataloguing in Publication Data
A CIP catalogue record for this book is available from the British Library

ISBN: 978-1-40939-266-8

MIX
Paper from
responsible sources
FSC   FSC™ C018179
www.fsc.org

ALWAYS LEARNING   PEARSON

WELCOME TO PIGGY ISLAND

Piggy Island is home to a kingdom of egg-snaffling Pigs and a flock of Angry Birds who will do everything they can to protect their young from the ever-present threat to their offspring. You may be weary after your journey to this remote corner of the world, but this is no time to take to your perch. Turn the page to discover fun facts, gags and a wealth of piggy puzzles and angry activities designed to tease those brain cells. They'll help you decide once and for all whether you're a total birdbrain or one clever chick.

BIRDIE BIOGRAPHIES

Which Angry Bird lives for sweets and who has gone into retirement? Read on to find out who's who.

RED

Fearsome leader of the Flock, Red is the angriest of all the Angry Birds. His commitment and sheer Red-ication is a source of inspiration and he's always first in the slingshot.

CHUCK

Competitive Chuck is the fastest of the Flock and is Red's most loyal friend and ally. However, the yellow fellow's impetuous nature often lands him in birdie bother.

BOMB

Ka-booom! The clue's in the name: Bomb's egg-straordinary egg-splosions are devastating. However he is not fully in control of his powers, which makes his fellow Flock members nervous.

MATILDA

Spiritual Matilda is a hippy at heart. This nature-loving chick would love to find a solution where the Birds and Pigs could live side by side in ham-mony! But while the Pigs continue to threaten the eggs, Matilda will continue to snap.

JUST YOLKING!

Q: When's the best time to buy an Angry Bird?
A: When it's going cheep!

4

THE BLUES

Jim, Jake and Jay are three of a kind. This tricksy young trio love playing pranks, worship Red and the Mighty Eagle, but can be very immature and irresponsible at times.

STELLA

Feisty and feathery, Stella is one stubborn pink bird. She's fiercely independent and doesn't nest with the Flock, preferring to visit from time to time. Stella's very smart and loves thinking up new tactics to try to dupe the Pigs.

TERENCE

Terence's immense bulk, coupled with his self-imposed silence, make him a huge asset during an assault on the Pigs, and he cuts a terrifying figure in the slingshot. Intimidating and inscrutable – it is impossible to know what's going on in his head.

BUBBLES

Small and cute he may be, but don't be fooled. Bubbles has the ability to inflate himself into an enormous balloon, which wreaks havoc on pig fortresses. Like Terence, Bubbles is a bird of few words; in fact, the only time he opens his beak is to scoff sweets!

HAL

An open-minded adventurer, Hal lives outside the Flock too. He enjoys living on the sunny side of the island where he strums his banjo, but he drops in to visit the Angry Birds whenever he can.

MIGHTY EAGLE

Little is known of Mighty Eagle's life since his retirement. The heroic bird feels he let Red and the Flock down, and now lives as a hermit, becoming very grumpy when disturbed.

FEATHERY PHRASES

How many words or sentences can you make from the following phrase?

ANGRY BIRDS RULE THE SKIES

---   ---

---   ---

---   ---

---   ---

---   ---

---   ---

---   ---

---   ---

---   ---

---   ---

---   ---

DID YOU KNOW?

The Angry Birds may be irate, but at least they're not poisonous. The Hooded Pitohui songbird of Papua New Guinea has neurotoxins in its feathers, which can cause irritation or numbness if touched.

RANCID RULER WORDSEARCH

King Pig is certainly not the most appealing of creatures on Piggy Island. Some of his most oinkful characteristics are listed below. Can you locate them in the grid?

P	E	T	T	Y	R	A	G	R	E	D	Y	T
S	L	N	A	I	D	R	X	T	Y	R	N	Y
H	U	A	T	Y	T	E	P	Q	U	A	R	R
E	F	I	S	E	L	K	E	F	T	W	V	A
L	T	E	E	D	D	E	E	R	T	A	N	N
P	I	V	G	R	I	D	O	E	G	Y	S	N
L	E	N	T	T	E	P	F	E	S	Z	T	I
E	C	S	A	O	M	L	U	D	E	A	A	C
S	E	T	V	I	U	O	H	T	F	L	P	A
S	D	U	F	B	V	L	A	Z	S	W	I	L
L	E	L	I	N	F	E	N	T	I	E	L	S
E	E	T	R	I	N	F	A	N	T	I	L	E
S	S	S	E	L	T	H	G	U	O	H	T	S

Deceitful	Tyrannical	Self Important	Lazy
Greedy	Stupid	Thoughtless	Naive
Infantile			Petty

Another less than attractive characteristic is hiding in the grid, find it and write the word below.

___ ___ ___ ___ ___ ___ ___ ___

CRAZY CHARACTER CROSSWORD

How well do you know the island's inhabitants?
Put your beak to the test with this crazy crossword.
Simply work out each character's name from the
clues below and fill in the grid.

ACROSS:

1. They're the lowest of the low, but these lowly porkers will do all they can to find eggs for the King. (6, 4)

3. He's the scariest ball of feathers; just don't expect him to talk! (7)

5. The angriest of the Angry Birds and top egg protector. (3)

7. Owner of the most distinguished beak in the kingdom. This guy's banjo is never far away. (3)

8. Fill in the gaps. _ _ _ _ man 'Boss' Pig sports a fetching moustache. (4)

9. The island's most prankalicious pals. Jim, Jay and Jake are better known as the _ _ _ _ _. (5)

10. With an empty egg chamber and an almighty ego, he's a right royal swine. (4)

12. This bird's a great friend, and if you don't like him at first, he'll grow on you. Literally! (7)

DOWN:

1. A nature-loving lady, this bird is absolutely peck-fect – until she snaps! (7)

2. She's fiercely independent, and a bit of a drama queen. (6)

4. King Pig is also known as Smooth _ _ _ _ _ _. (6)

6. Faster than any other critter on the slingshot, he's loyal, but his quick decisions often land him in trouble. (5)

9. With a short fuse, this bird's explosive nature surprises everyone, including himself! (4)

11. Scheming and clever, this pig is always cooking up new plans to become King. (4)

WHO AM I?

Solve the riddle to find the Flock member.
Then write their name below.

I'm small and I'm cute,
But don't get me wrong,
I'll be much bigger than this,
Before too long.
I never talk much,
and I love all things sweet.
Sometimes I've a mouthful,
So can't caw nor tweet.

I'm _____

JUST YOLKING!

Q: What do Pigs and Angry Birds need when they're sick?
A: Oinkment and tweetment!

THE MINION PIG HUNT

Your help is urgently required; the Minions' moody monarch has ordered them to find him eggs, pronto! Unfortunately the silly swine couldn't find their way out of a paper bag, never mind a Piggy Island maze! Can you help them locate the eggs?

SCRAMBLED EGGS

The Angry Birds of Piggy Island weren't always angry – nor were they always birds. Once upon a time they were merely eggs themselves. Can you unscramble the names on the eggs to work out who hatched from each?

1  ------------------------

2 ------------------------

3  ------------------------

4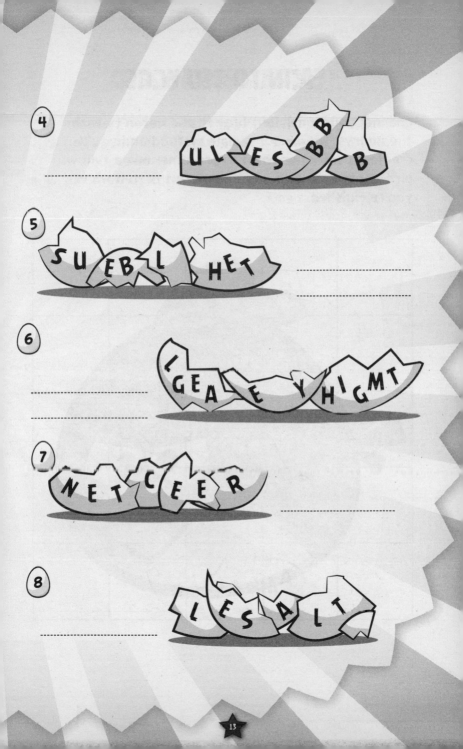

U L E S B B B

_____

5

S U E B L   H E T

_____

_____

6

L G E A E Y H I G M T

_____

_____

7

N E T C E E R

_____

8

L E S A L T

_____

13

LEARN TO DRAW RED

Channel your inner Red-brandt and get arty with the Angrys. Follow our simple method and you'll create a perfect portrait every time! Get a fellow bird-spotter to give you a mark out of ten when you're finished.

WHAT TO DO:
Copy the picture of Red into the grid below,
concentrating on the details contained in one
grid-square at a time.

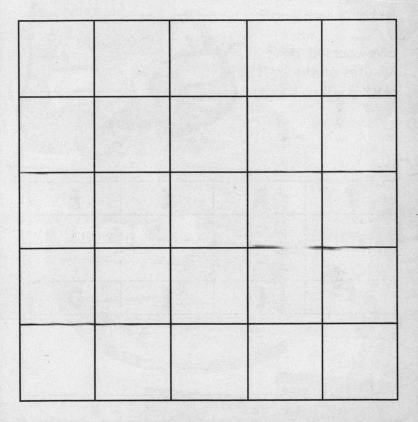

PROFESSOR PIG'S WORD BOXES #1

Professor Pig can solve these word-box puzzles in a flash. Can you get from the word at the top to the word at the bottom, by changing just one letter in each word?

Give yourself three minutes on the clock – GO!

T	R	E	E
F	L	E	D

SLINGSHOT SCRAMBLE

The Angry Birds just can't wait to go after their eggs. Three members of the Flock are scrambling to be first in the slingshot, but who are they?

1. ....

2. ....

3. ....

HAL'S BANJO BREAKDOWN

Always up for an adventure, Hal's at his happiest exploring Piggy Island's hidden coves, caves and crevices! But cunning Chef Pig has hidden Hal's beloved banjo! Solve the riddles to reunite Hal with his instrument.

RIDDLE 1

I'm big and I'm bold, I take up lots of room,

But don't get too close or I might just go boom!

Who am I?

RIDDLE 4

There was a time when I was brave, a hero of the land.

Now, instead my own space, peace and quiet I demand!

Who am I?

RIDDLE 3

Big and scary, you won't get a word out of me.

I go about my birdie business and do it silently.

Who am I?

RIDDLE 2

I'm seriously stubborn and, boy, am I cross!

I'll protect the Flock's eggs, whatever the cost.

Who am I?

PIGGY-FUL EFFORT

Foreman Pig's incompetence has come back to haunt him. His latest construction has collapsed. Exactly how many blocks and planks are burying him?

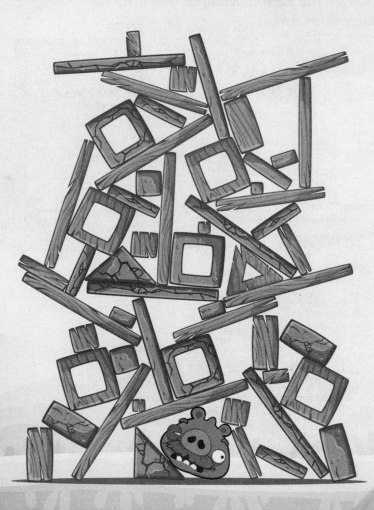

HOME TWEET HOME

Scheming Chef Pig is one of the more intelligent pigs. He's on the trail of the Angry Birds and is trying to follow them home. Circle every sixth letter to discover the barren, mountainous area where the Angry Birds dwell.

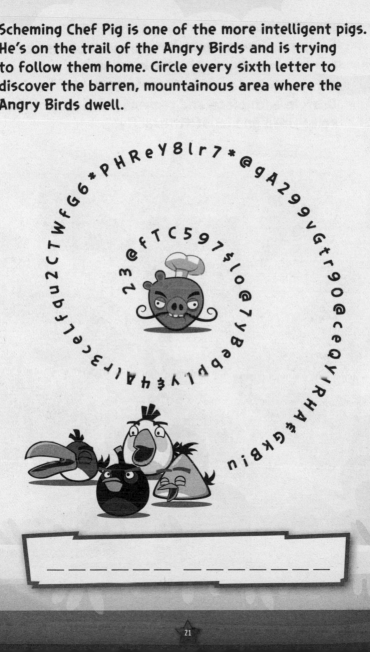

K IS FOR KING

K is for King and don't you forget it! King Pig was having this letter nailed to the wall of his castle, but Foreman Pig botched the job and it shattered. Can you help Foreman Pig rebuild it for the King? Draw in each piece and remember - every bit has to be used and must fit exactly.

WHOSE BEAK IS IT ANYWAY?

These beaks were made for squawking, and that's just what they'll do . . . Can you work out which Angry Birds' beaks are shown below?

This beak belongs to

This beak belongs to

This beak belongs to

This beak belongs to

This beak belongs to

THE WHOLE HOG

Screaming squealers! This just takes the bacon; a slice of Corporal Pig is missing. Can you tell which of the sections below will make him whole again?

1.   2.   3.   4.   5.   6.

BIRDIE BRAIN STRAIN

When it comes to logic do you rule the roost or are you a total birdbrain? Test your smarts with these riddles. Think carefully – there may be more than one solution!

RIDDLE 1

How can you fling an Angry Bird as hard as you can and have it come back to you, even if it doesn't bounce off anything, has nothing attached to it and no one catches or throws it back to you?

RIDDLE 2

Four Angry Birds are sitting in a very leafy tree wearing party hats; they know that two of them have blue hats and two of them have yellow hats, but they're not allowed to take their hats off to see which colour they are wearing. Who will be the first to guess the colour of his own hat? Given that:

1. Red is sitting on the top branch and can see both Bomb and Chuck below him.

SUPER HARD

2. Bomb can see Chuck sitting below him, but can't see Red.

3. The tree is so leafy Chuck can see neither Red nor Bomb above him.

4. Hal is at the base of the tree obscured from view by a thicket of branches – he can't see any birds nor can any bird see him.

Hint: There are two possible answers.

OH PECK!

Terence has accidentally perched his huge bulk on some words and smashed them to smithereens. Look at the word fragments below. Can you find a longer word these leftover letters might fit into? There may be more than one option for each. The first one is done for you.

a sp fo ati
meri to sh nic con er in p d

NGUE	toNGUE	meriNGUE
1. LLEL		
2. ICNIC		
3. ATULA		
4. HEP		
5. ERSAT		

PROFESSOR PIG'S WORD BOXES #2

Here's another of Professor Pig's favourite word-box puzzles. Can you get from 'cast' to 'fame', by changing just one letter each time?

Put three minutes on the clock. Ready, birdie, go!

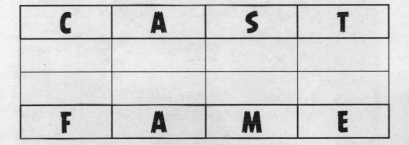

C	A	S	T
F	A	M	E

SPOOKY SPOT THE DIFFERENCE

It's Halloween on Piggy Island and the Pigs are hoping
to freak the Angry Birds out so much they'll flee their
nest and leave their eggs unattended.

Can you spot eight differences between the pictures below?

PIG OUT

Unable to successfully steal the Angry Birds' eggs, the Pigs exist on a vegetarian diet. How many grass-munching Minions can you spot in the meadow?

SUFFERING SUDOKU

The Pigs take an almighty beating from the Birds on an almost daily basis. Draw in more shattered and battered piggies to fill up this Sudoku grid. Make sure each of the Pigs features only once in each row, column and four-by-four box.

BIRD BATH

The Pigs are amazed by soap bubbles floating on the breeze, but which member of the Flock is hiding in the foam-filled sky?

PRANK YOU VERY MUCH

Jim, Jake and Jay love to play pranks, and while Bomb slept they've fenced him into a tangle of squares and rectangles. Count how many there are before Bomb blows.

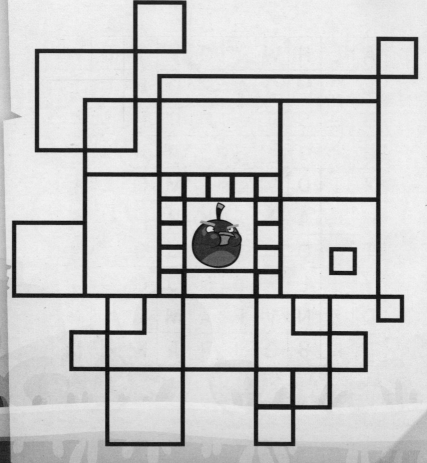

MULTIPLE MAYHEM

Pigs who put a trotter out of line can find themselves catapulted from the ramparts of King Pig's vast castle. Who's been ousted this time? Cross out the letters of the alphabet that feature more than once and rearrange those left over to discover the identity of the latest porky victim.

A	L	H	W	J	O	Y	T	Q	W
V	D	M	Q	U	N	O	R	B	L
B	O	S	F	M	O	J	B	S	Y
R	V	J	L	S	E	A	N	X	T
X	I	D	R	O	L	M	Q	C	L
N	K	A	T	A	K	R	U	U	K
T	Z	O	M	J	Q	U	G	Q	S
Y	S	L	R	O	U	O	O	D	M
D	Z	N	V	P	A	M	L	S	O
A	K	B	O	J	R	A	N	U	M

ANGRY ANAGRAMS

The ever-present threat to their offspring means
the Birds on Piggy Island aren't just angry, they're
apoplectic with rage. There are lots of words that
mean angry. Unscramble these anagrams to
find them – then circle the one word with the
opposite meaning.

DAM

CARYZ

DIVIL

MALC

SOFUURI

GUMFIN

GRENADE

NICESEND

WHATFURL

SORCS

RATIE

STY Q TEST

King Pig suspects the Minion Pigs are too stupid to steal the eggs. So Chef Pig has devised this 'Squeal Wheel' test to check their intelligence. Fill each empty segment in the outer circle by multiplying the number in the centre with the number in the inner circle. This Minion has managed to do the first one on his own. Come on! You have one minute!

PROFESSOR PIG'S WORD BOXES #3

We're back with the Professor's favourite type of puzzle. This time there are five steps to make, changing a letter each time, but you have to find every word using the clues.

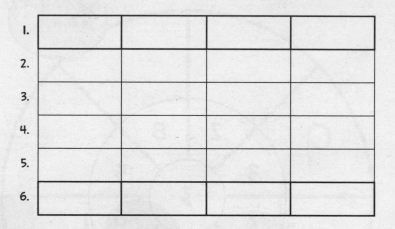

1.				
2.				
3.				
4.				
5.				
6.				

1. A word that describes what you do with a book.
2. A word meaning the back of something; another word for rise.
3. Grizzly, black and brown are types of this animal.
4. A wild pig.
5. Angry Birds do this when they're in the air.
6. To make something completely wet.

BIRTHDAY BOMB

It's Bomb's birthday and all the excitement has made him explode! How many of his gifts have been caught up in the blast? Write your answer below.

PIG PREDICTION

Chronicler Pig interprets the laws of the herd. Unfortunately he is getting old and can't crack his own codes any more. Can you help him read this prediction about King Pig? Use the key below to work out what it says.

A	B	C	D	E	F	G	H	I
#	Ø	$	π	Œ	✓	≈	ʃ	Δ

J	K	L	M	N	O	P	Q	R
@	+	Σ	∞	~	Å	»	Ɛ	*

S	T	U	V	W	X	Y	Z
ọ	=	Ω	§	%	¥	ə	₱

∂Å𝛺   O∫#ΣΣ   ØŒ

§Δ$=Å*ΔÅ𝛺O̲   #~∏

O̲∫#ΣΣ   √Œ#O̲=   Å~

Œ≈≈O̲   √Å*

∂Œ#*O̲   =Å $Å∞Œ

MINION'S MISSING NUMBERS

Pig constructions involve many tools and equations. Can you help this Minion Pig find the missing numbers on the rungs?

?

48

?

31

24

18

13

9

6

4

CHUCK GETS CHUCKED

Chuck is soaring above a massive fortress. How many pieces are in this complex construction?

SHUT IN

One sandwich short of a pig-nic as always, these silly Minions have built a fortress so complex they've accidentally bricked themselves in. There is one way out; can you help them find it?

RED ALERT

King Pig has issued a 'Wanted' poster for the Flock's leader to be distributed among the Minions. Sadly only one of the images is a faithful de-pig-tion of Red. Can you tell which? Circle the real Red.

SPOT THE BIRDIE

Test your powers of pigs-ervation with this quick picture quiz. Give yourself one minute to drink in every detail of the picture on the right. Then cover the picture and try to answer the questions below.

1. How many Pigs are in the picture?

   ----

2. Besides Red, which other Angry Birds are on the beach?

   ----

3. What is Red brandishing?

   ----

4. What piece of Pig mining equipment is floating in the water?

   ----

5. How many seashells can you see on the beach?

   ----

6. Which Pig is floating in the life-ring?

   ----

7. How can you tell?

   ----

8. How many eggs are in the picture?

   ----

9. Does the Pig under the water have one black eye or two?

   ----

10. Is the Pig in the life-ring's tongue hanging out to the left or right?

SNUFFLING SEQUENCES

This little piggy went to build a fortress, this little piggy stayed at home in his castle . . . The Pigs are all going about their business, but can you see who comes next in each sequence?

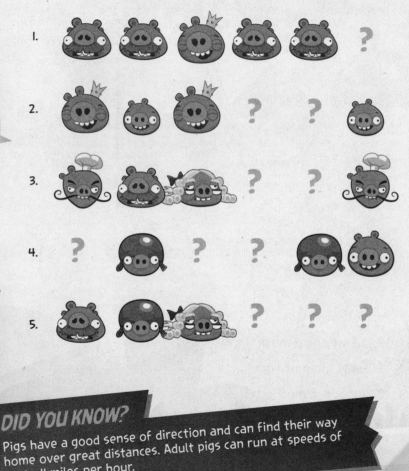

THERE'S ONLY ONE . . .

The Flock's leader is totally unique – there's only one Red. The answer to each of statements below features the word 'ONE'. Your task is to add 'ONE' to a different letter or letters to make a new word. Check out the picture of Red for help in solving the first clue.

1. You eat ice cream from this.   ....one

2. A dog might enjoy this.   ....one

3. Finished.   ....one

4. Not any.   ....one

5. Quality of a musical or vocal sound.   ....one

6. Small lump of rock.   ....one

7. A modern method of communication.   ....one

8. By oneself.   ....one

STY Q TEST

This Minion is really worried! Can he complete the 'Squeal Wheel' portion of King Pig's Sty Q Test and avoid being catapulted from the castle ramparts? Help him fill each empty segment in the outer circle by multiplying the number in the centre with the number in the inner circle. You have just 60 seconds.

FLORA AND FAUNA

As well as its fauna (namely the Pigs and the Angry Birds) Piggy Island is home to all sorts of flora. Can you find part of a flower in the words below?

THE KING'S TRUMPET ALERTED THE PIGS

LETTER SEARCH

The Angry Birds often ask Bomb to stand guard over their eggs. Some of the letters of the alphabet are missing from this egg. Find the missing letters and arrange them to make an egg-related word.

G
S
P
U
O
D M E
I
N X C
B
H R J
F Q T Z
V
K W

CHUCK'S MATHS CHALLENGE - LEVEL 1

Competitive Chuck wants to know how quickly you can complete this maths puzzle. Set a timer and follow the instructions. Fill the grid with numbers from 1 to 3 without repeating numbers in any row or column. 'Cages' are the boxes outlined in bold. You must fill each cage with numbers that add up to the target number in the corner using the maths symbol given, so a 5+ will mean the digits in that cage must add up to five.

Time taken to complete ....

BIRDOKU BEGINNERS

In the aftermath of the latest bombardment there are birds bouncing everywhere. Can you get them in some sort of order within this number grid? The object is to fill in the remaining squares so each row, column and four by four box contains each of the numbers from one to four.

		4	
1	4		
			4
	3		

CHEF'S WORDSEARCH

While waiting for the Minions to come back with some eggy spoils, Chef Pig wiles away his time by imagining all the ways he could prepare and serve the eggs. Can you find his favourite egg recipes in the grid?

O	E	U	S	E	N	G	E	G	B	N	O	G	E
U	E	F	O	D	E	L	B	M	A	R	C	S	F
F	U	U	L	S	P	A	C	H	E	D	L	A	B
S	O	U	F	F	L	É	D	E	V	L	E	D	O
F	F	O	S	S	A	N	W	G	I	P	R	C	I
B	S	U	U	F	E	S	O	V	O	X	I	S	L
A	H	C	F	B	A	N	B	A	M	Q	O	T	E
D	C	O	F	Y	E	X	C	A	E	U	M	R	D
E	U	C	L	G	W	H	S	O	L	S	E	D	E
K	S	L	E	O	E	E	B	F	C	P	L	M	I
A	T	E	S	D	V	A	A	R	Y	O	E	B	F
B	A	V	C	Y	K	M	K	I	R	O	T	A	R
S	R	E	R	D	F	R	E	E	D	C	T	T	I
E	D	E	L	L	I	V	E	D	K	H	E	R	E

1001 Egg Recipes

- Baked
- Boiled
- Custard
- Devilled
- Fried
- Oeufs en cocotte
- Omelette
- Scrambled
- Poached
- Soufflé

CLOUD GAZING

Spiritual chick Matilda loves nature and finds inner peace cloud gazing. Can you write down the names of the fluffy-looking friends and foes she can spot in the sky?

SUMMER SUMS

Water, waves, boats . . . it must mean a day at the beach! Each letter in this seaside puzzle represents a different number from 0 to 9. Can you work out which number each letter represents and solve the sum? Hint: A=2, O=3, T=4, E=6 and R=7.

		W	A	T	E	R
+		W	A	V	E	S
+			B	O	A	T
	1	6	9	9	6	0

SUPER HARD

HIDE AND CHEEP

Diligent Chuck likes to exercise in order to be in tiptop slingshot condition for forthcoming missions. Find another word to describe what Chuck does to prepare, which is hidden in the phrase below.

SOME EXTRA INK

MORE MINION'S MISSING NUMBERS

Can you help this Minion up the ladder to the top of the fortress by finding the missing numbers on the rungs?

SUPER HARD

?

19,683

?

2,187

729

?

81

27

9

3

WHO AM I?

It'll be a real feather in your cap if you can work out the mystery bird from this little ditty.

I'm focused and yellow,
A fast little fellow,
I'm loyal as peck, don't you know?
I reduce blocks to rubble,
But can get into trouble,
For acting impusively, though.

Who am I? _____

CHRONICLER PIG'S QUICK QUIZ

Can you ace Chronicler Pig's True/False quiz?
Circle the T if you think the fact is perfectly
correct and the F if it's a huge porky pie.

1. Foreman Pig is a
brilliant engineer.

T/F

2. King Pig's main worry is that he'll
be overthrown by Chef Pig.

T/F

3. The Minion Pigs are generally
very happy with their lives.

T/F

4. The only Pig with facial
hair is Foreman Pig.

T/F

5. King Pig's full name is
King Pig Smooth Cheeks.

T/F

6. Corporal Pig is able to lead large troops of Minion Pigs.

T/F

7. Pigs are great swimmers and can easily catch the Angry Birds in water.

T/F

8. In King Pig's luxurious castle there is a huge throne room filled with tapestries of the pig royal family.

T/F

9. The Pigs live in Swinesville.

T/F

10. When Pigs don't have eggs to eat they survive on fruit.

T/F

CROSS DIGITS

This puzzle is as cross as Red in an empty nest.
It works just like a crossword but you'll need to get
your head in the maths zone!

ACROSS:

2. 2 x 91
4. 68 ÷ 2
5. The sum of 7 across and 14 down
7. One third of 66
8. 1,001 + 242
10. 52 ÷ 4
12. Number of months in a year, doubled
13. Half of 3,536
15. 7 x 3
16. 26 + 26 + 13
17. 100 – 4
18. 417 + 99

DOWN:

1. 54 ÷ 3
2. You have a dozen eggs and are given a further two. How many eggs do you have?
3. Half of 5,842
4. One third of 17 across
6. 21 x 4.
7. 9 down minus 90.
9. 123 reversed.
11. 1131 x 5.
14. 152 ÷ 2.
15. 10 across doubled.
17. 70 + 11 + 15.
19. 75 ÷ 5.

SUPER HARD

PORKY PICS

Red has been keeping an eye on the Pigs' activities. Can you work out who he's looking at?

A

B

C

D

COLOSSAL COLOUR-IN

Terence is notorious amongs the Angry Birds for his sheer bulk. Can you match his impact on paper as you shade in the sections (marked with symbols contained in the key) below? Grab a red pencil and bring Terence to life.

KEY

+ = light red
@ = medium red
* = dark red

DID YOU KNOW?

Terence is the largest of the Angry Birds, measuring over 175 BMUs (Bird Measurement Units), but did you know that the bee hummingbird is the world's smallest bird at just 5cm long?

MERRY DIFFERENCES

Santa Claus is coming to town and the Angry Birds watch in wonder (while the Bad Piggies panic about whether they're on the naughty list) as his sleigh

zooms across the night sky over Piggy Island. There are ten differences between the picture on the left and the one on the right. Can you spot and circle them all?

THE SWINE LINE

Some of these Pigs are in a pickle. In each line someone is missing something. Can you spot the odd one out in each line of swine?

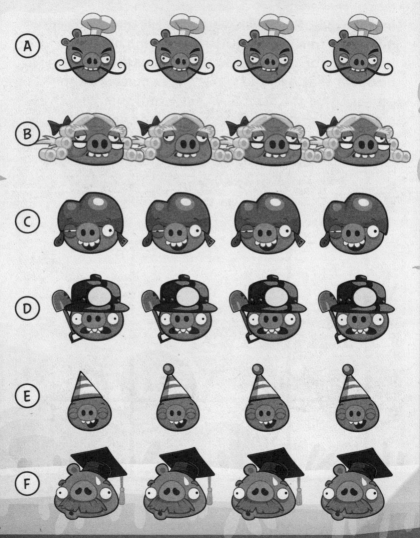

CHUCK'S MATHS CHALLENGE - LEVEL 2

Chuck's back with the next level of his maths challenge. Set a timer and then follow the instructions. Here's what you do: fill the grid with numbers from 1 to 4 without repeating numbers in any row or column. You must fill each cage with numbers that add up to the target number in the corner using the maths symbol given, so a 4+ will mean the digits in that cage must add up to 4.

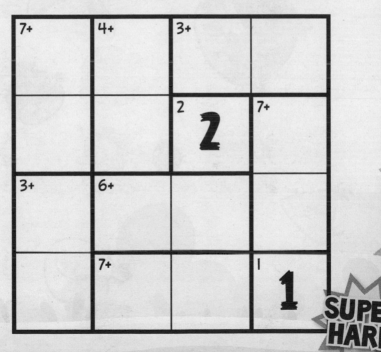

Time taken to complete ....

BIRDOKU INTERMEDIATE

So you survived beginner level Birdoku– let's see if you can take it up a notch. This time the numbers I to 6 must appear in each row, column and three-by-two box.

2	1			4	3
		6	2		
		3	4		
3	4	2		5	6

TRICKY TRAJECTORIES

The slingshot is yours, but how accurate are you?
Use a pen or pencil to draw in the trajectory or flight
path from each slingshot so Chuck and Red smash this
fortress.

DID YOU KNOW?

The Angry Birds' missions are perilous but as long as they protect
their eggs they won't face extinction. The Dodo is a famously
extinct species of bird. The last one died in 1681.

STY Q TEST

It's the terrifying 'Squeal Wheel' portion of King Pig's Sty Q Test again, and this pig is mired in the mud when it comes to arithmetic. Can you help him fill each empty segment in the outer circle by multiplying the number in the centre with the number in the inner circle?
You have just 60 seconds or it's the sausage factory for you and your porky pal!

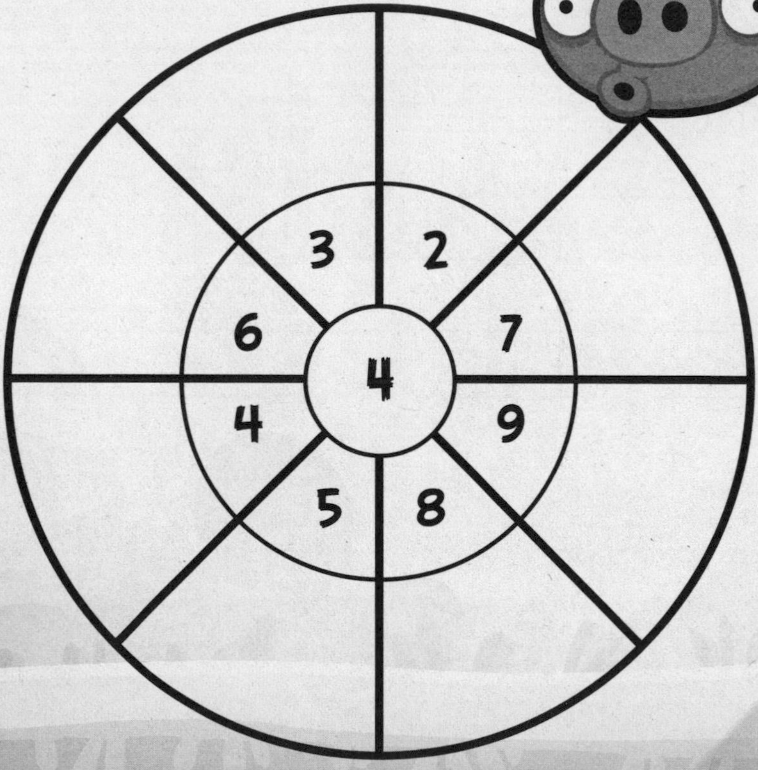

3 2

6 7

4

4 9

5 8

PROFESSOR PIG'S WORD BOXES #4

Professor Pig's favourite word-box puzzles just got tougher. Can you get from 'dark' to 'pest' by changing one letter each time? Fly into action!

D	A	R	K
P	E	S	T

GRILLED BACON # 1

Here's the latest tricky puzzle in King Pig's Sty Q Test. It involves the points of the compass so you'll need all your orienteering skills to help you and the Minions with this one.

Use the compass directions below to help you correctly place the missing letters of the alphabet in the grid. Remember that 'North' or 'South' means any location along the same column and 'East' or 'West' means any location along the same row.

DIRECTIONS:

- A IS EAST OF K; C IS NORTH OF P
- B IS WEST OF N; Y IS WEST OF E
- D IS EAST OF L; G IS WEST OF W
- F IS NORTH OF T AND WEST OF Q
- H IS NORTH OF S AND EAST OF I
- I IS NORTH OF J; K IS NORTH OF X
- J IS SOUTH OF E AND EAST OF T
- L IS SOUTH OF E; Q IS EAST OF I
- M IS WEST OF D AND SOUTH OF Z
- P IS WEST OF J AND NORTH OF M
- R IS NORTH OF T; U IS EAST OF P
- S IS NORTH OF N AND EAST OF P
- V IS SOUTH OF Y AND WEST OF T
- W IS SOUTH OF Y; X IS WEST OF T

HIDE AND CHEEP

None of these foodstuffs are on the Angry Birds' menu, but can you find the name of a wild animal lurking within?

BROCCOLI, ONION, RADISHES

THE BLUES' THREE IN ONE

I. Which three-letter word is hiding here?
Tick the correct box.

COT ☐   GOT ☐   CAT ☐   GET ☐

2. Circle the odd number out.

913, 747, 1692, 8449

3. What is special about this sentence?

MADAM, I'M ADAM.

PUZZLE BRIDGE

Help Corporal Pig cross the bridge by answering the questions on each section. You may only move forward a step if you answer correctly. No cheating!

1. What **N** is a circular structure built from twigs and leaves that houses the Angry Birds' eggs?
2. What **G** forms the major part of the Pigs' diet?
3. What **P** is home to the Angry Birds and the Bad Piggies?
4. What **S** is the tool the Angry Birds use to launch themselves at the Pigs?
5. What **C** is a type of fortress and the abode of King Pig?

6. What **D** is an explosive material often used by the Pigs in caves and mines?

7. What **B** is a sandy area found on the coast of Piggy Island?

8. What **M** is another word for assignment or task – as undertaken by the Angry Birds?

9. What **H** is a piece of metal headgear worn by Corporal Pig?

10. What **F** describes the gender of Matilda and Stella?

ESTIMATE GUESSTIMATE

Whee! It's a very windy day on Piggy Island and anything that's not hammered to the ground is blowing freely in the breeze. Without counting, you must guess the following:

- The number of slingshots on the page.
- The number of Angry Birds on the page.
- The number of daisies on the page.
- The number of dots on the page.
- The number of stars on the page.
- The number of stones in the crowns on the page.

Now check the answers and see how close you got!

DID YOU KNOW?

A homing pigeon's powers of observation are second to none. The clever creatures are able to assess the magnetic flow of the earth, the angle of the sun, and star patterns to help guide them home.

WHO AM I?

So feminine me, with my rosy
pink cheeks,
Communing with nature
I spend days and weeks,
I'm spiritual, see.
I'm a sensitive type,
But don't get me mad or you'll
see it's not just hype.
Yes, my eggs they are lethal,
whenever they drop
I'll destroy any fortress
from bottom to top.

Who am I?

ANGRY-CROSSY-GRAMS #1

These puzzles are bizarre enough to make you explode like Bomb. Write the clues into the grid. It doesn't matter what order you put the letters in, but they must fit both across and down.

ACROSS	DOWN
1. Mood	1. Pool
2. Long	2. Gong
3. Lone	3. Lend
4. Pong	4. Moon

	1	2	3	4
1				
2				
3				
4				

TACITURN TERENCE

It's very hard to know what's going on with Terence because he almost never speaks. Use the pictures to decipher his innermost thoughts.

THAT [pig king] IS A [donut] .

[pigs] WILL NOT [cut] **T** [cake]

[birds] [nest with eggs] .

EVEN MORE MINION'S MISSING NUMBERS

Help this Minion find his way up the ladder by working out the missing numbers on the rungs. To do this you'll need to work out the mathematical pattern. For example 6 x 3 = 18, 18 ÷ 2 = 9, etc.

SUPER HARD

?

18

90

?

60

12

?

9

18

6

HAM SOUP

The Pigs are taking a mud bath and there are so many in the pool it's like a massive tureen of ham soup! How many Minions can you spot?

HAM SANDWICH

Eeek! This porker's surrounded by an angry mob. Join the dots to discover the piggy in the middle.

DID YOU KNOW?

The world's heaviest recorded pig came from Taiwan. It weighed more than 908kg (143 stones) - around 20 stones heavier than the average adult hippo!

STY Q TEST

Hurrah! It's the final 'Squeal Wheel'. Can you help this Minion complete the puzzle? You know the rules by now. Remember, you've only got 60 seconds in which to finish this, so you'd better be multiplication mad!

8 1

6 4

9

3 9

5 7

THE BLUES' THREE IN ONE . . . AGAIN

1. Which three-letter word is hiding here?
   Tick the correct box.

FIN ☐   FUN ☐   SUN ☐   SUM ☐

2. What do these words have in common?

SPLASH, SIZZLE, CUCKOO.

3. Unscramble the letters to find the Angry Bird.

CENTREE

GRILLED BACON #2

Professor Pig is really grilling the Minions with the questions on King Pig's compulsory Sty Q Test. Use the compass directions below to help you correctly place the missing letters of the alphabet in the grid. Remember that 'North' or 'South' means any location along the same column and 'East' or 'West' means any location along the same row.

DIRECTIONS:

- A IS SOUTH OF L: D IS WEST OF W
- E IS EAST OF C; G IS SOUTH OF W
- B IS WEST OF W AND NORTH OF H
- F IS NORTH OF Z AND WEST OF R
- H IS EAST OF T AND WEST OF Y
- I IS NORTH OF U AND EAST OF C
- L IS NORTH OF F; P IS EAST OF Z
- M IS EAST OF J; O IS WEST OF N
- N IS SOUTH OF C AND EAST OF Z
- Q IS NORTH OF J; R IS SOUTH OF C
- S IS EAST OF F; U IS WEST OF J
- V IS WEST OF J AND NORTH OF N
- X IS NORTH OF U
- Y IS SOUTH OF W AND EAST OF N

CAVING CLOSE-UPS

The Pigs need a lot of equipment for their cave excavations. Foreman Pig is making an inventory, but he's zoomed in too close with his camera. Can you identify the underground objects from the extreme close-ups?

Pit helmet
Umbrella
Crate of dynamite
Gold coins
Lantern
Spade
Pickaxe
Crystal
Stalactite

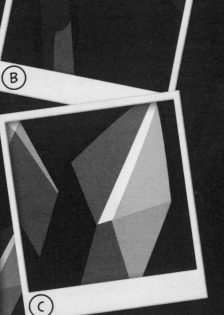

B

A

C

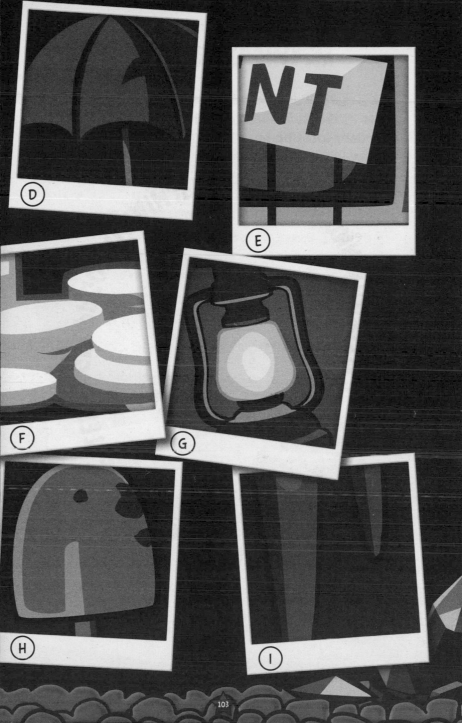

MYTHICAL MARKINGS

Take a marker and circle or underline every ninth letter in this sequence to find a mythical and legendary location near Piggy Island.

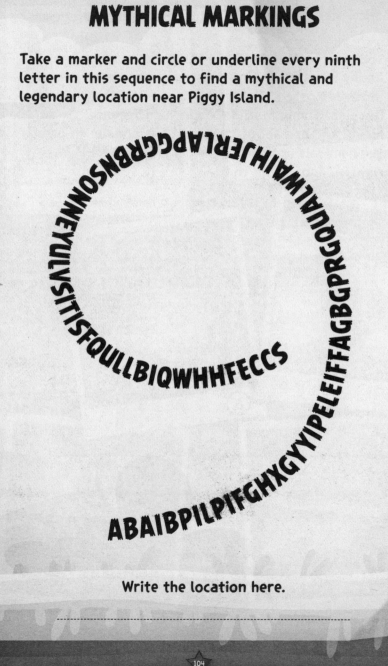

Write the location here.

ANNUAL BIRDIE FLING-OFF

Today's the Annual Birdie Fling-off, in which the Angry Birds pit their strength against each other in the slingshot. The bird who goes furthest wins. Bubbles, Bomb, Matilda, Chuck and Terence all scored highly and are about to mount the podium to collect their medals from Red. Can you draw them in their rightful spot given that:

- Bubbles went the third furthest and Bomb came second.
- Matilda was not last.
- Terence didn't win.
- Matilda came after Bomb.

DID YOU KNOW?

Birds really have been awarded medals. During the First World War a pigeon named Cher Ami saved the lives of many soldiers by carrying a message across enemy lines in the heat of battle. He was awarded the Croix de Guerre for heroic service.

GRILLED BACON #3

Compass time again. Help the Minion Pig pass the latest part of the Sty Q Test created by Professor Pig. Use the compass directions below to help you correctly place the missing letters of the alphabet in the grid. 'North' or 'South' means any location along the same column and 'East' or 'West' any location along the same row.

DIRECTIONS:

- A IS SOUTH OF M; C IS EAST OF O
- B IS WEST OF Y AND NORTH OF S
- D IS WEST OF O; F IS EAST OF X
- E IS NORTH OF U AND WEST OF L
- G IS WEST OF L; K IS NORTH OF D
- H IS NORTH OF X AND WEST OF L
- I IS NORTH OF C AND EAST OF Y
- P IS SOUTH OF B; Q IS NORTH OF J
- N IS EAST OF R AND SOUTH OF L
- R IS SOUTH OF Y; V IS NORTH OF W
- S IS SOUTH OF G AND WEST OF O
- U IS SOUTH OF Y AND WEST OF W
- W IS EAST OF O AND SOUTH OF L
- X IS WEST OF J AND EAST OF R
- Z IS WEST OF Y AND NORTH OF K

MAKE SURE YOU FIND THE NAME OF A VOLCANO IN ITALY WITHIN THIS GRID. IF YOU DON'T HIS MAJESTY WILL BE VERY CROSS!

			L		
	Y				
				J	
		O			

FRUITY FEAST

Yum! it's beak-fast time on Piggy Island and the Birds are having a fruity feast. You have 30 seconds to check out what's on the menu today. Then cover the picture and write the names of the fruit as they appear from left to right.

HIDE AND CHEEP

The Angry Birds are a pretty special species with amazing powers, including the ability to go underwater. Find a watery place within the sentence below.

UMBRELLA KEPT FOR BAD WEATHER

CROSS DIGITS

This puzzle is as cross as Red in an empty nest. It works just like a crossword but you'll need to get your head in the maths game!

ACROSS:

2. Number of days in a leap year
4. 10 across minus 5 across
5. 30 – 3
7. A dozen expressed as a number
8. 1,235 reversed.
10. 5 x 10
12. 4 x 6
13. 901 + 210
15. 16 across minus 12 across
16. 5 x 10 + 4
17. Number of days in 8 weeks
18. Half of 250

DOWN:

1. 3 x 4 down
2. A quarter of 132
3. 1,247 x 5
4. 17 + 5
6. 6 x 7 across
7. 13 across divided by 11
9. 200 – 80
11. 4,181 re-arranged
14. 5 across minus 7 across
15. 6 x 6
17. Half of 110
19. 10 across minus 15 across

SQUEAL WHAT YOU SEE

This puzzle is simple: it's simply a case of verbalizing the visual – as in, say out loud what you see. Each box contains a common phrase or saying; can you work out what they are?

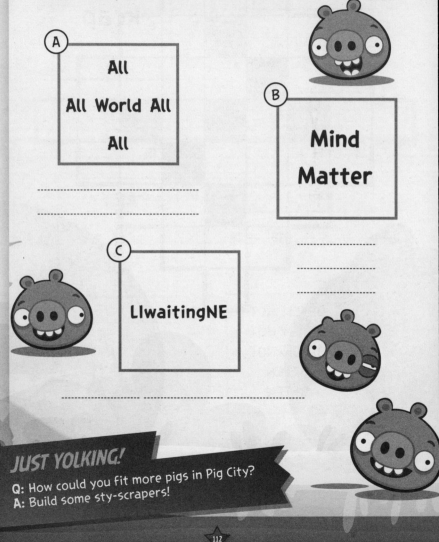

A

All

All World All

All

---------------- ----------------
---------------- ----------------

B

Mind

Matter

C

LIwaitingNE

---------------- ---------------------- ----------------

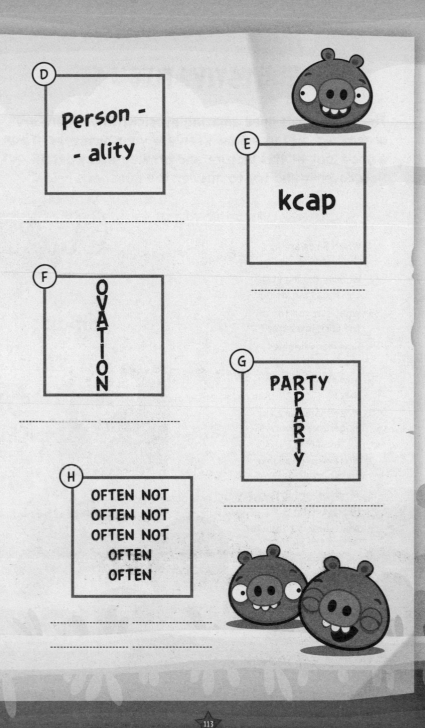

D

Person -
- ality

E

kcap

F

OVATION (vertical)

G

PARTY
PARTY (vertical)

H

OFTEN NOT
OFTEN NOT
OFTEN NOT
OFTEN
OFTEN

FESTIVE FUN

The Angry Birds need amazing eyesight when there are greedy pigs at large. How keen are your own eyes? Take a good look at this picture and drink in every detail. Now cover it and try to answer the questions below.

1. Which Birds are in the picture?
2. What is the Pig in the Christmas hat doing?
3. What's at the top of the Christmas tree?
4. How many baubles are there?
5. How many eggs are there?
6. What shapes are the gingerbread cookies on the tree?
7. What else is hanging on the tree?
8. Which other Pig is in the picture?
9. Which Bird is to the far left of the picture?
10. Which Bird is nearest the Christmas tree?

JUST YOLKING!

Q: What song do pigs sing on New Year's Eve?
A: 'Auld Lang Swine!'

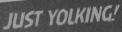

JIGGLED GEOGRAPHY

Think you know Piggy Island? Well, take a stroll around with Chef Pig as your guide and try to unravel the different exotic locations this land has to offer.

GIP TICY

1 --

Chef's Clue: Urban hangout for swine.

HOUST ACHEB

2 --

Chef's Clue: Sandy spot where items wash in from the ocean.

LATBOC TEAULAP

3 --

Chef's Clue: Flat area of land that's good for nesting.

OGH DAHE NOMUNATI

4 --

Chef's Clue: Mound of rock shaped to look like King Pig. Full of trails leading to the Hot Springs.

GIP SENIM NAD SACEV

5 --

Chef's Clue: Underground area full of stalagmites and crystals where the Pigs store gold.

THE BLUES' THREE IN ONE . . .
ONCE MORE

1. Which three-letter word is hiding here?
   Tick the correct box.

BAG ☐   BAN ☐   BOG ☐   BEN ☐

2. Rearrange the letters to find an ancient creature
   birds are said to evolve from.

ARDONISU

3. If a female pig is a sow, what is a male pig?

WHO AM I?

The Flock always welcomes
A visit from me.
I come from exotic climes,
to sit in a tree.

I strum my best tunes,
To see my friends' smiles,
Or show them my beak,
The biggest by miles.

Who am I?

CHEF'S SPECIAL WORD GRID

So can you ace Chef's special word grid? Look at the letters within the grid and then answer the questions. You may only use each letter once!

E	P	B
M	C	D
N	I	O

1. Put a tick beside the word below that appears in the grid

   INN ☐   ODD ☐   ICE ☐   PET ☐

2. Put a tick beside the word below that is not in the grid

   DINE ☐   NICE ☐   DICE ☐   NOSE ☐

3. Can you find a seven-letter word meaning to put together (as Chef might do with ingredients in a recipe)?

PIGSONALITY TEST

What's your pigsonality? Take this pigsonality test to find out. First use this page to draw a pig and *do not* look at the next four pages until you've finished your picture. Your pig can be as creative or as plain as you want. Now get drawing!

Piggy Pose: you've drawn your pig at the top of the page.

Piggy Island Pigsonality – like the **Minion Pigs** you're an optimist with a positive attitude. You generally anticipate the best possible outcomes of actions and events. In other words, you see the glass as half full.

Piggy Pose: your pig is drawn toward the bottom of the page.

Piggy Island Pigsonality – like **Chef Pig** you tend to be more pessimistic and like to make your own secret plans.

Piggy Pose: your pig is drawn towards the middle of the page.

Piggy Island Pigsonality – you are a realist like **Red** who tends to face facts and deal with them. You see the glass as dirty but you put it in the dishwasher.

Piggy Pose: your pig is drawn facing left.

Piggy Island Pigsonality – like **Matilda**, you believe in tradition, and are friendly, outgoing and sensitive to others.

Piggy Pose: your pig is drawn facing right.

Piggy Island Pigsonality – you are innovative and active and easy going – like **Hal.**

Piggy Pose: your pig is drawn facing forward.

Piggy Island Pigsonality – you're easy to read and straightforward, like **Bomb.**

Piggy Pose: your pig is drawn with many details.

Piggy Island Pigsonality – you are analytical, cautious, careful and may be distrustful, like **Chronicler Pig.**

Piggy Pose: your pig is drawn with few details.

Piggy Island Pigsonality – like **the Blues** you are impulsive and playful.

Piggy Pose: Your pig is drawn with 4 legs showing.

Piggy Island Pigsonality – you're like **Foreman Pig**. You are secure, rule-bound and can be stubborn.

Piggy Pose: Your pig is drawn with fewer than 4 legs showing.

Piggy Island Pigsonality – like **Corporal Pig** you may be insecure but you are very loyal.

Piggy Pose: Your pig has large ears.

Piggy Island Pigsonality – like **Terence**, you don't say much, but you take it all in and make a good listener.

Piggy Pose: You drew a long tail on your pig.

Piggy Island Pigsonality – you are cute and independent and love to be loved – just like **Stella**.

PIGS IN BLANKETS

Did you know the Pigs love Halloween? It gives them a chance to try to scare the Angry Birds away from their eggs.

One little Minion has forgotten his ghost costume. Can you find him?

UNDERGROUND OVERGROUND

The Pigs are trying to get to the nest of eggs by tunnelling underground. Which path will take them to the eggs rather than directly to an Angry Bird?

TRICKY TRIANGLES

Defending their precious eggs requires the Angry Birds to be mentally on the ball. Keep your noggin in good shape with this brainteaser. How many triangles can you see in the shapes below?

I see _____ triangles.

CHUCK'S MATHS CHALLENGE - LEVEL 3

Let Chuck take you under his wing and guide you through his Maths Challenge, which is now even trickier. This time you may need to multiply (*) or divide (/) the digits to reach the target number in the corner of each cage. Remember you need to fill the grid with numbers from 1 to 4 without repeating numbers in any row or column.

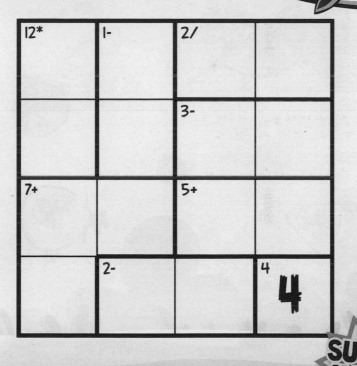

12*	1-	2/	
		3-	
7+		5+	
	2-		4 **4**

Time taken to complete _____

SUPER HARD

BIRDOKU MASTERCLASS

You floated through the beginner- and intermediate-level Birdoku like an Angry Bird on the breeze. Now, before you get too big for your beak, let's see if you can ace Birdoku Masterclass. Like the previous instalment the object is to fill in the remaining squares so every row, column and three-by-three box contains the numbers 1 to 9. Good cluck!

7				6			2	
	3	2	9	7	5			
	6	5		4	3			
6	8					7	1	
1	7					9		5
9	5					2	8	
	4	8		2		1		
	1	3	5	6		4		
5				1			3	

CONNECT THE CAVE CONQUERORS!

The crazy world of Piggy Island isn't just skin deep. Far below the surface, crews of cave-lurking pigs are busy tunnelling, mining and generally going about their piggy business. Connect the dots to see how these subterranean swine look!

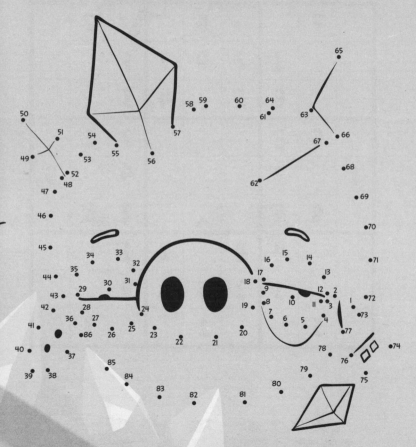

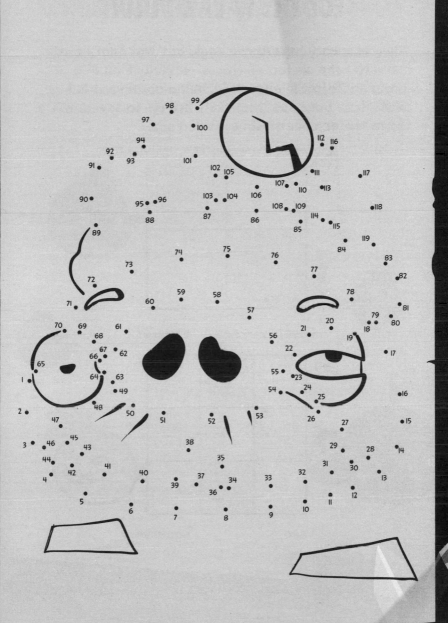

LOOK CAW-CAW-FULLY!

They may only have three eggs, but the Angry Birds need to keep on top of things on Piggy Island in order to keep the eggs safe. Being observant is key. Make sure your spotting skills are up to speed; write down the number of squares you see.

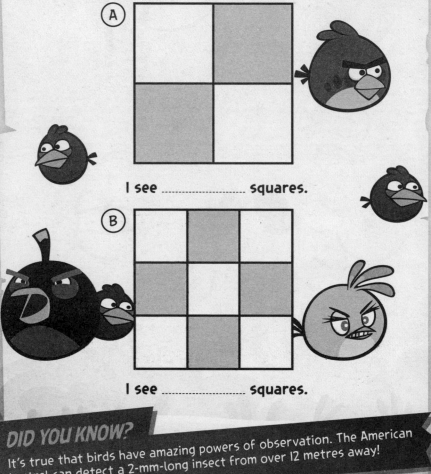

A

I see _____ squares.

B

I see _____ squares.

SWEET DREAMS, BUBBLES

Candy-crazy Bubbles is fast asleep. He's dreaming he's buried in gorgeous creamy toffees. Can you spot him and count how many treats are filling his subconscious?

MATILDA MAGIC

1. What special power does Matilda wield during bombardments of fortresses?

----

2. Can you name the ancient oriental art Matilda practises to balance the energies of the nest?

   NEST _ _ _ _

3. Which of these is not one of Matilda's passions?
   Organic cooking   Sewing   Gardening   Meditating

4. Besides anyone threatening the eggs,
    what makes Matilda angriest of all?

    ....

5. Which Flock members sometimes accuse Matilda of
    smothering them with her maternal behaviour?

    ....

SCHOOL'S OUT!

Red's decided to teach his birdie crew some lessons! Show him you are paying attention by spotting the eight differences between pictures A and B.

ANGRY-CROSSY-GRAMS #2

Bomb might just fly off the handle if you can't solve his latest angry-crossy-gram puzzle. Write the clues in the grid; the thing is the letters shouldn't and won't fit in order. It doesn't matter how you put the letters in, but they must fit both across and down.

ACROSS

1. Erupt
2. Nymph
3. Horse
4. Soaks
5. Twist

DOWN

1. Risky
2. Heath
3. Spoon
4. Strum
5. Swept

LAND LOVER'S LETTER LINK

Now's your chance to show off your knowledge of Pig City. It's a vast section of land, strewn with abandoned structures and inventions created to help King Pig find the eggs.

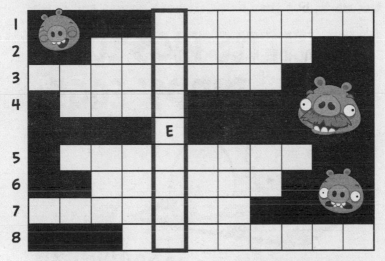

1. Name of the area the Pigs live in. (3,4)

2. Name of the moustache-sporting pig who co-ordinates all pig constructions. (7)

3. Smelly and squidgy places where the pigs love to bathe. (3,5)

4. Culinary-loving pig who lives next to King Pig. (4)

5. Yummy pork-based food, eaten with mash – this is a rude word to pigs. (8)

6. Fortified building and home to King Pig. (6)

7. The lowliest type of pig... (7)

8. Sparkly rocks the pigs find in their mine and caves. (8)

The letters in the central column will reveal the name of a key pig character. Here's a clue to his identity . . .

This intellectual pig wears glasses and creates brilliant inventions to help improve the Pigs' quality of life. (9)

TASTE TEST

This pig is literally foaming at the mouth in anticipation of the taste of a yummy egg. He can't wait to crack open the shell and scoff the lot. How many words or phrases can you make from this phrase?

LITTLE PIGS LOVE BIRDS' EGGS

TRICKIER TRIANGLES

Time for more shape-spotting fun with Red and his PFFs (that's pecking friends forever). Check out the shape below and write down how many triangles you see in total.

I see _____ triangles.

BEWARE THE OCTOPIG

Courageous Red is trying to escape the clutches of the giant Octopig. Can you help him through the maze of Piglantis to the safety of the shore?

SLEEPY STELLA

Stella is so worn out from being rebellious ALL the
time that she's had to stop for a quick nap.
Draw a ring round snoozing Stella.

HAPPY HOGGYDAYS

Everyone in Pig City loves the hoggyday season; crisp, snowy mornings, gingerbread cookies and brightly lit Christmas trees. King Pig has received many cards from his loyal subjects. Here's one of them. Use the code to decipher the greeting.

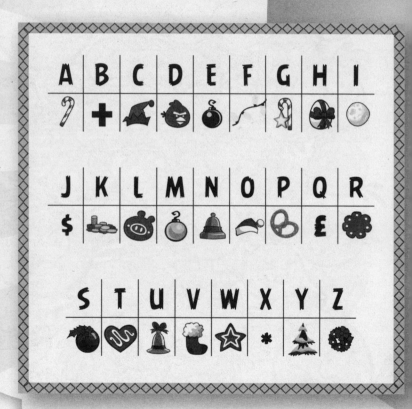

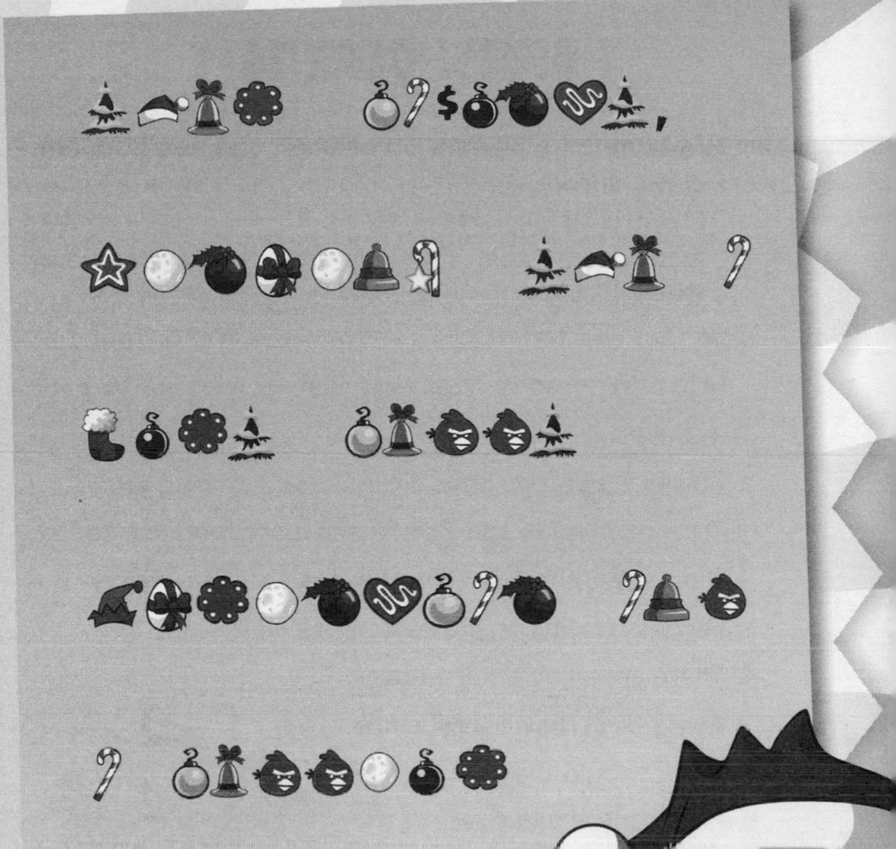

BLUES' BERRIES

Jim is sitting on a pile of 40 berries, can you help him work out the following?

1. He needs to keep a quarter of the stash back in case of a bad fruit harvest. How many should he put aside?

2. Of that quarter, he will put 20% back in the ground to help next season's crop. How many berries will he put in the soil?

3. How many berries does Jim now have to give away?

4. Terence, Matilda and Bomb need more food due to their size. They'd like four berries each. How many berries remain for the rest of the Flock?

5. There are eight other hungry Angry Birds: how many whole berries could they have each?

6. How many would that leave as a snack for the Mighty Eagle?

THE BLUES' WORD BOXES

Here we go again. Get this puzzle right and the Blues will offer their hearty congratulations! There are five steps to make, changing a letter each time. Use the clues to help you.

1.				
2.				
3.				
4.				
5.				
6.				

1. The opposite of smooth.

2. Something you do when you have a chest cold.

3. _ _ _ _ _ potato – name for a lazy person.

4. Kangaroos carry their young in one of these.

5. If you kill wild animals that don't belong to you; also a way to cook eggs.

6. Entrance area in front of a main door.

EASTER FEASTER

This wily pig has disguised himself as the Easter Bunny in order to get close to the Angry Birds' eggs and he seems to have pulled it off.

JUST YOLKING!

Q: The Pigs love celebrations, especially Valentine's Day, but who sends them Valentine's cards?

A: Cupig!

Copy him square by square into the empty grid below before he starts scoffing.

DOT TO DOPES

Doh! What are these dozy pigs up to on Halloween?
Join the dots to find out.

SECRET SCRAWLS

Although the Angry Birds can't read or write, King Pig insists that all correspondence between pigs is done in code – just in case. Can you work out what's contained in this secret note? You'll need to swap each letter of the alphabet for the letter that comes straight after it; so an A should be swapped for a B etc.

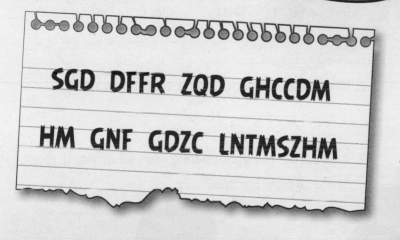

SGD DFFR ZQD GHCCDM

HM GNF GDZC LNTMSZHM

SIMPLY STELLA

She's the new chick in town, having only recently hooked up with the Flock. How much do you know about bubbly Stella?

1. Which of these is not one of Stella's character traits?

   Independent   Feisty   Smart   Insecure

   ---

2. What accessory does Stella sometimes wear?

   ---

3. Apart from the egg-stealing Pigs, what might cause Stella to blow her top?

4. What might Stella do if an older bird told her off, or challenged her?

----

5. What colour are Stella's feathers?

SUPER HARD

BIRDIE KITES

On sunny days the Angry Birds love nothing better than a picnic in a meadow. Can you unravel the strings to discover which leads to the kite Terence is flying?

YOU TAKE THE CAKE!

Look at the scrumptious sweet treats on this page; don't they look delicious? Have a really good stare and then turn the page . . .

YOU TAKE THE CAKE - PART II

Now take a look at the cakes again. A greedy pig has snaffled an item. Can you tell which, without turning back to the first picture?

POWER CUT

There's been a power cut in Pig City. Can you tell who's who from just their silhouettes?

WHO AM I?

A loner am I,
Yet I'm part of the tribe,
I'm grumpy, ashamed and
I won't take a bribe,
I'm not going to tell you,
Just what I have done.
I've failed, I feel guilty,
The Flock I must shun.

QUICK TRIVIA:

- WHO IS BEING DESCRIBED?
- TO WHAT FOODSTUFF IS HE ADDICTED?
- WHERE DOES HE LIVE?

Draw a picture of this mysterious character for
the Blues, who hero-worship him.

PIGGY ISLAND MASH UP

Can you tell which of these Piggy Island inhabitants have morphed into each mutant creature? Write their names in the spaces.

---   ---

--   --

DID YOU KNOW?

Pigs have such a well-developed sense of smell they can easily find things underground. In France they're used to locate and dig up valuable truffles.

MATILDA'S MENTAL MATHS

Matilda's one big bird and these are some big numbers. Put your maths skills to the test with these massive sums...

1,009 x 2 + 500,000 - 16 + 7,841 =

540 + 400 + 8,006 + 792 =

6,005 - 9 x 2 + 300 + 54 =

100,000 ÷ 2 x 100 =

600,000 + 14 + 533 =

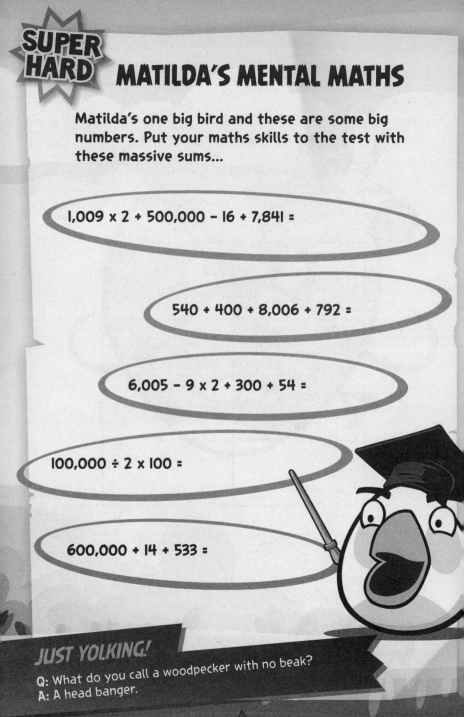

JUST YOLKING!

Q: What do you call a woodpecker with no beak?
A: A head banger.

LOOK MORE CAW-CAW-FULLY

Take a bird's-eye view at this square below.
How many squares can you see in total?

I see _____ squares.

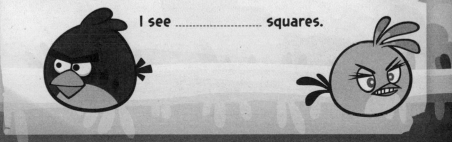

CAN YOU PIP THE PROFESSOR?

Professor Pig is the most intellectual pig on Piggy Island but he wasn't at all sure about the answers to these questions about the wider world and only got one right. Can you better his paltry score?

1. Who painted *The Mona Lisa*?

----

2. How many wives did King Henry VIII of England have?

3. Which ship sank on her maiden voyage in 1912?

4. Where does the Prime Minister of the UK live while in London?

DID YOU KNOW?

Did you know that pigs communicate constantly with one another? More than 20 piggy sounds have been identified. Mother pigs even 'sing' to their young while nursing.

5. Which businessman founded Virgin Records and Virgin Airlines?

----

6. What colour are daffodils?

----

7. What's the innermost colour of a rainbow?

----

8. What has the scientific formula H_2O?

----

9. Which is the only vowel not on the top row of a computer keyboard?

----

10. Ping-Pong is an alternative name for which sport?

PIGGY FORTUNES

If Corporal Pig was surrounded by piles of gold, he's so daft he'd think it was worthless. What he'd really like is this gorgeous gift-wrapped egg. It's the most important prize on Piggy Island. Can you help him scoop it?

WE ASKED 100 MINIONS TO ANSWER THE FOLLOWING:
Can you guess what they said?

1. Name something you do when you've finished eating a meal.

2. Name a nocturnal animal.

3. Name something you can see but you cannot touch.

4. Name something you might take to the beach.

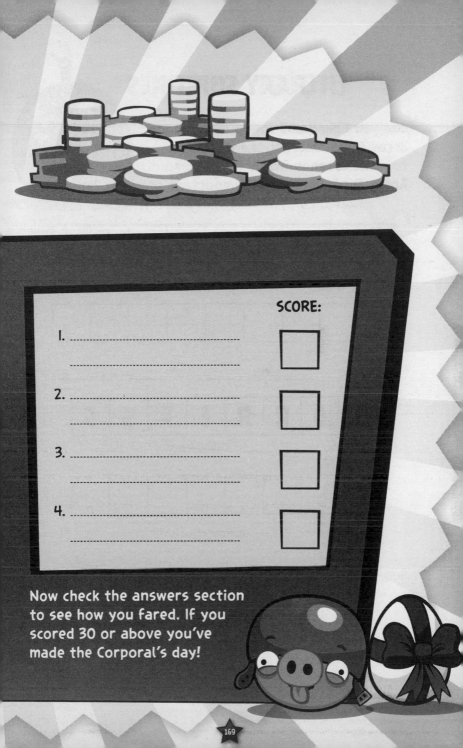

SCORE:

1. _____
   _____ ☐

2. _____
   _____ ☐

3. _____
   _____ ☐

4. _____
   _____ ☐

Now check the answers section to see how you fared. If you scored 30 or above you've made the Corporal's day!

LITERARY SHIFT

Can you help Bomb follow the arrows and re-order the letters to make common words in the Angry Birds vocabulary?

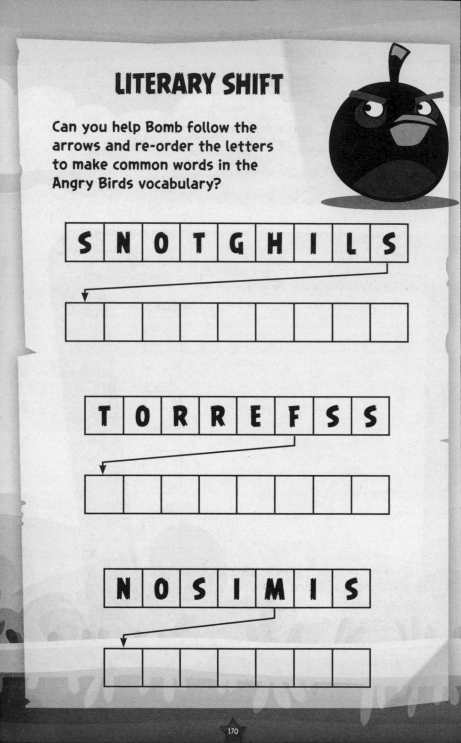

S	N	O	T	G	H	I	L	S

T	O	R	R	E	F	S	S

N	O	S	I	M	I	S

BOSS'S BLOCKS

SUPER HARD

Foreman 'Boss' Pig is building one of his 'impenetrable' walls! Can you help the hapless pigster work out . . .

How many more blocks it will take his Minions to complete the design.

The area of each block – given that each block measures 5 x 10mm.

• the area of each block.   ---

• the total area of the finished wall ---

TRICKIEST TRIANGLES

Oooh! This final, difficult shape-spotting conundrum might ruffle your feathers. How many triangles in total can you see? Pick up a pen and get quacking!

I see _____ triangles.

CHEF'S SPECIAL WORD GRID

Look at the letters within the grid and then answer the questions. You may only use each letter once!

D	B	N
U	O	R
W	F	E

I. Put a tick beside the word below which appears in the grid.

FIN ☐   FUN ☐   BUT ☐   BET ☐

2. Put a tick beside the word below which is not in the grid.

HOUR ☐   BORN ☐   WORN ☐   FORE ☐

3. Can you find a seven-letter word meaning glowered
(as Red might do at the Pigs)?

SEEING RED

He's the angriest of the Angry Birds, but what makes him tick, tock and blow his top? Test your knowledge of the Flock's figurehead.

I. Describe Red in three words.

----

2. Does he have any flaws?

----

3. Which other member of the Flock does he most resemble?

----

4. What would Red do to protect the eggs?

5. What does Red see as his ultimate long-term goal?

----

6. Who is Red's right-hand bird?

7. Red has a difficult relationship with one
of the Flock. Who and why?

SWINE CRIME!

The Pigs never miss an opportunity to grab the Angry
Birds' eggs, even on special days. Check out the scene

below, then use the space to write a report to the Mighty Eagle about the latest swine crime.

BIRDIE BEACHCOMBING

Several items have washed up on the beach. Can you tell what they are from these bird's-eye views?

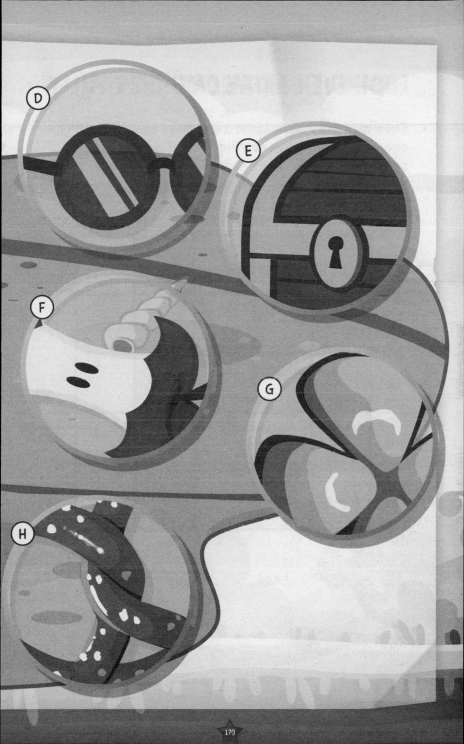

LOOK EVEN MORE CAW-CAW-FULLY!

They may only have three eggs, but the Angry Birds need to keep on top of things on Piggy Island in order to keep the eggs safe. Being observant is key. Make sure your spotting skills are up to speed; write down the number of squares you see.

I see .... squares.

JUST YOLKING!

Q: What kind of bird can open doors?
A: A kiwi.

ANSWERS

Page 7 Rancid Ruler Wordsearch

P	E	T	T	Y							T
	L			D						N	Y
H	U				E				A		R
E	F					E	T				A
L	T		D			R					N
P	I			I		O		G	Y		N
L	E	N			P				Z		I
E	C		A	M		U		T	A		C
S	E		I				T	L		A
S	D		F	V			S			L
	L			E					
	E			I	N	F	A	N	T	I	L	E
S	S	S	E	L	T	H	G	U	O	H	T

The extra adjective is HELPLESS.

Pages 8-9 Crazy Character Crossword

Page 10 Who Am I?
Bubbles

Page 11 The Minion Pig Hunt

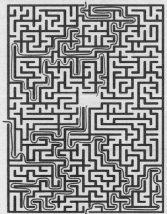

Pages 12-13 Scrambled Eggs
1. Chuck
2. Red
3. Matilda
4. Bubbles The Blues
5. Terence
6. Mighty Eagle
7. Stella

Page 16 Professor Pig's Word Boxes #1

T	R	E	E
F	R	E	E
F	L	E	E
F	L	E	D

Page 17 Slingshot Scramble
Matilda, Chuck & Bubbles

Pages 18-19 Hal's Banjo Breakdown
Riddle 1 - Bomb
Riddle 2 - Red
Riddle 3 - Terence
Riddle 4 – Mighty Eagle

Page 20 Piggy-ful Effort
57

Page 21 Home Tweet Home
Cobalt Plateau

Pages 22-23 K is for King

Page 24 Whose Beak Is It Anyway?
Stella   Matilda   Bomb   Bubbles   Chuck

Page 25 The Whole Hog
5

Pages 26-27 Birdie Brain Strain
Riddle 1:
Throw Hal, the boomerang bird.
Riddle 2:
Either Red or Bomb would be the first to
work out the colour of their own hat:

1. If Bomb and Chuck have hats of
   the same colour, then Red will see
   and immediately say his own colour
   (different to theirs).
2. If Bomb and Chuck have different
   coloured hats, then Red will remain
   silent and that would be a signal to
   Bomb, who by looking at Chuck will
   know what his own colour is, i.e. the
   colour Chuck is not wearing.

Page 28 Oh Peck!
1. Tongue; Meringue
2. Parallel; Hallelujah
3. Picnic
4. Spatula; Congratulations
5. Shepherd; Heptagon
6. Conversation; Versatile

Page 29 Professor Pig's Word Boxes #2

C	A	S	T
C	A	S	E
C	A	M	E
F	A	M	E

Pages 30-31 Spooky Spot the Difference

Pages 32-33 Pig Out
57

Page 34 Suffering Sudoku

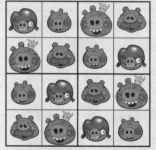

Page 35 Bird Bath
Stella

Page 36 Prank You Very Much
38

Page 37 Multiple Mayhem
Chef Pig

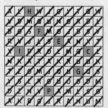

Page 38 Angry Anagrams
Mad Crazy Livid Furious Incensed
Fuming Enraged Wrathful Cross Irate
The word with the opposite meaning is
'calm'.

Page 39 Sty Q Test

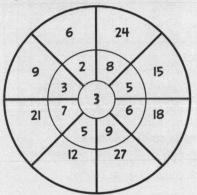

Page 40 Professor Pig's Word Boxes #3

R	E	A	D
R	E	A	R
B	E	A	R
B	O	A	R
S	O	A	R
S	O	A	K

Page 41 Birthday Bomb
64 presents are caught up in Bomb's blast.

Pages 42-43 Pig Prediction
Chronicler Pig says:

YOU SHALL BE VICTORIOUS AND SHALL FEAST
ON EGGS FOR YEARS TO COME

Page 44 Minion's Missing Numbers
4 6 9 13 18 24 31 39 48 58

4 (+2) =6 (+3) =9 (+4) =13 (+5) =18 (+6)
=24 (+7) =31 (+8) =39 (+9) =48 (+10) =58

Page 45 Chuck Gets Chucked
104

Page 46 Shut In

Page 47 Red Alert
D

Pages 48-49 Spot the Birdie
1. Two
2. Bomb and the Blues
3. A trident
4. TNT (dynamite)
5. Two
6. King Pig
7. He is wearing his battered crown.
8. Three
9. Two
10. To the right (or to his left).

Page 50 Snuffling Sequences

Page 51 There's Only One . . .
1. Cone.   2. Bone.   3. Done.   4. None.
5. Tone.   6. Stone.   7. Phone.   8. Alone.

Page 52 Sty Q Test

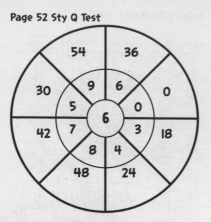

54 36 30 9 6 0 5 6 0 42 7 3 18 8 4 48 24

Page 53 Flora And Fauna

THE KINGS' TRUM**PET AL**ERTED THE PIGS

Page 54 Letter Search

Lay

Page 55 Chuck's Maths Challenge Level I

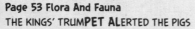

3+		5+
1	2	3
5+ 3	**1** 1	2
2	**4+** 3	1

Page 56–57 Birdoku Beginners

3	2	4	1
1	4	2	3
2	1	3	4
4	3	1	2

Page 58-59 Chef's Wordsearch

O						E	G	G	N	O	G	
	E			D	E	L	B	M	A	R	C	S	
		U										B
S	O	U	F	F	L	E						O
			S						P			I
			E				O					L
				N		A				O		E
D	C					C				M		D
E	U			H		O			E		
K	S			E		F	C		L		
A	T		D			R		O	E		
B	A					I			T		
	R					E			T	T	
	D	E	L	L	I	V	E	D			E		E

Pages 60–61 Cloud Gazing

A. Red. **B.** Minion Pig. **C.** King Pig.
D. Stella. **E.** Chuck. **F.** Hal.
G. Corporal Pig. **H.** Chef Pig.

Page 62 Summer Sums

	8	2	4	6	7
+	8	2	1	6	9
+		5	3	2	4
	1	6	9	9	6	0

A=2; B=5; E=6; L=0; O=3; R=7; S=9; T=4; V=I;
W=8

Page 63 Hide and Cheep

SOME EX**TRA IN**K

Page 64 More Minion's Missing Numbers

**3 9 18 27 81 243 729 2,187 6,561 19,683
19,683 59,049**

**3 (x3) =9 (x3) =27 (x3) =81 (x3) =243 (x3)
=729 (x3) =2,187 (x3) =6,561 (x3) =19,683
(x3) =59,049**

Page 65 Who Am I?

Chuck

Pages 66-67 Chronicler Pig's Quick Quiz

I. False. Foreman Pig is a terrible engineer.
2. False. King Pig's main worry is that his
    subjects will discover his empty egg
    stash.
3. True
4. False. Chef Pig also has a moustache.
5. True

6. False. He can only lead four Minions at a time.
7. False. They can't swim and hate water.
8. True
9. False The Pigs live in Pig City.
10. False. The Birds eat fruit. The Pigs eat grass.

Pages 68-69 Cross Digits

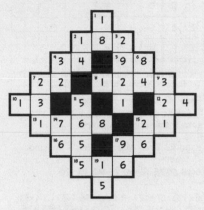

Page 70 Porky Pics

A. Foreman Pig
B. Chronicler Pig
C. Corporal Pig
D. King Pig

Pages 72-73 Merry Differences

Page 74 The Swine Line

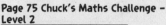

Page 75 Chuck's Maths Challenge – Level 2

7+	4+	3+	
4	3	1	2
		2	7+
3	1	2	4
3+	6+		
1	2	4	3
	7+		1
2	4	3	1

Pages 76-77 Birdoku Intermediate

2	1	5	6	4	3
6	3	4	5	1	2
4	5	6	2	3	1
1	2	3	4	6	5
5	6	1	3	2	4
3	4	2	1	5	6

Pages 78-79 Tricky Trajectories

Page 80 Sty Q Test

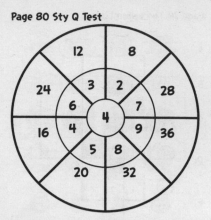

Page 81 Professor Pig's Word Boxes #4

D	A	R	K
D	A	R	T
P	A	R	T
P	E	R	T
P	E	S	T

Pages 82-83 Grilled Bacon No. 1

	C	Y	R	E	O	
K	Z	A	F	I	H	Q
X	P	V	T	J	S	U
G	M	W	B	L	N	D

The European city is Paris.

Page 84 Hide and Cheep #2
BROCCOLI, ONION, RADISHES

Page 85 The Blues' Three in One
1. Cat
2. 1,692 is the only even number
3. It's a palindrome – a phrase that can be read the same way backwards or forwards.

Pages 86-87 Puzzle Bridge
1. Nest; 2. Grass; 3. Piggy Island; 4. Slingshot; 5. Castle; 6. Dynamite; 7. Beach; 8. Mission; 9. Helmet; 10. Female.

Pages 88-89 Estimate Guesstimate
6 slingshots
18 Angry Birds
43 daisies
75 dots

22 stars
12 stones

Page 90 Who Am I?
Matilda

Page 91 Angry-crossy-grams #1

	1	2	3	4
1	O	O	D	M
2	O	G	L	N
3	L	N	E	O
4	P	G	N	O

Page 92 Taciturn Terence
"That King Pig is a donut. Pigs will not take the Angry Birds' eggs.

Page 93 Even More Minion's Missing Numbers
6 18 9 36 12 60 15 90 18 126

6 (x3) =18 (÷2) =9 (x4) =36 (÷3) =12 (x5) =60 (÷4) =15 (x6) =90 (÷5) =18 (x7) =126

Pages 94–95 Ham Soup
100

Page 96–97 Ham Sandwich
It's Foreman Pig.

Page 98 Sty Q Test

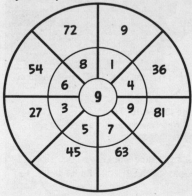

Page 99 The Blues' Three in One . . . Again
1. Fun
2. They are examples of onomatopoeia –

meaning they sound like the thing they describe.

3. Terence

Pages 100–101 Grilled Bacon #2

	L	C	I	Q	E	
D	F	R	X	B	W	S
K	A	V	U	J	G	M
O	Z	N	T	H	Y	P

River Danube

Pages 102–103 Caving Inventory

A. Pit helmet
B. Pick axe
C. Crystal
D. Umbrella
E. Crate of dynamite
F. Gold coins
G. Lantern
H. Spade
I. Stalactite

Page 104 Mythical Markings

Piglantis

Page 105 Annual Birdie Fling-off

1st Chuck
2nd Bomb
3rd Bubbles
4th Matilda
5th Terence

Pages 106–107 Grilled Bacon No. 3

	G	E	H	L	Q	
Z	B	Y	T	V	M	I
K	P	R	X	N	J	F
D	S	U	O	W	A	C

Etna is the Italian volcano. It's located in Sicily.

Page 108 Fruity Feast

L-R Watermelon, apple, strawberry, cherry, banana

Page 109 Hide and Cheep

UMBREL**LA KE**PT FOR BAD WEATHER

Pages 110–111 Cross Digits

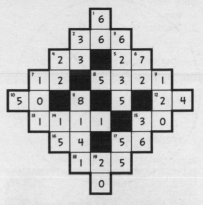

Pages 112–113 Squeal What You See

A. All around the world
B. Mind over matter
C. Waiting in line
D. Split Personality
E. Backpack
F. Standing Ovation
G. Tea Party
H. More Often than not

Pages 114–115 Festive Fun

1. Red, Bomb and the Blues
2. Eating a cookie meant for Santa
3. A star
4. Six (two partially visible)
5. Three eggs
6. Stars and the face of a pig
7. Three candy canes
8. Corporal Pig
9. Blue
10. Bomb

Pages 116 Jiggled Geography

1. Pig City
2. South Beach
3. Cobalt Plateau
4. Hog Head Mountain
5. Pig Mines and Caves

Page 117 The Blue's Three in One . . Once More
1. Bag
2. Dinosaur
3. Boar

Page 118 Who Am I?
Hal

Page 119 Chef's Special Word Grid
1. Ice
2. Nose
3. Combine

Pages 124–125 Pigs in Blankets

Pages 126-127 Underground Overground

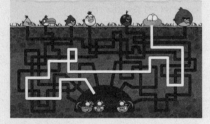

Page 128 Tricky Triangles
44 triangles

Page 129 Chuck's Maths Challenge – Level 3

12*	1-	2/	
4	3	1	2
3	2	3- 4	1
7+ 1	4	5+ 2	3
2	2- 1	3	4 4

Pages 130-131 Birdoku Masterclass

5	7	9	1	6	3	8	2	4
8	4	3	2	9	7	5	6	1
2	1	6	5	8	4	3	9	7
4	6	8	9	2	5	7	1	3
1	2	7	6	3	8	9	4	5
3	9	5	7	4	1	2	8	6
6	3	4	8	7	2	1	5	9
9	8	1	3	5	6	4	7	2
7	5	2	4	1	9	6	3	8

Page 134 Look Caw-caw-fully
5
14

Page 135 Sweet Dreams, Bubbles
101

Pages 135-136 Matilda Magic
1. She drops egg bombs.
2. Nest Shui
3. b. Sewing
4. Anyone who harms nature or the environment
5. To nurture the eggs
6. The Blues

Pages 138–139 School's Out

Page 140 Angry-crossy-grams #2

	1	2	3	4	5
1	R	E	P	U	T
2	Y	H	N	M	P
3	S	H	O	R	E
4	K	A	O	S	S
5	I	T	S	T	W

Page 141 Land Lover's Letter Link

	1	2	3	4	5	6	7	8	9
1				P	I	G	C	I	T	Y
2			F	O	R	E	M	A	N
3	M	U	D	P	O	O	L	S
4		C	H	E	F
				E
5		S	A	U	S	A	G	E	S
6			C	A	S	T	L	E
7	M	I	N	I	O	N	S
8				C	R	Y	S	T	A	L	S

Professor

Page 143 Trickier Triangles
27

Page 144 Beware the Octopig

Page 145 Sleepy Stella

Pages 146-147 Happy Hoggydays

Your Majesty,
Wishing you a very muddy Christmas and a
muddier New Year,
Corporal Pig

Page 148 Blues' Berries

1. 10 berries will be put aside.
2. 20% of 10 is 2, so two berries will go in the ground.
3. 30 berries will be left to distribute.
4. Terence, Matilda and Bomb will eat 12 berries. 30 – 12 = 18 berries left.
5. The other 8 Angry Birds would share 18 berries. 18 ÷ 8 = 2.25. So they could have two whole berries each.
6. This would leave two berries as a snack for the Mighty Eagle.

Page 149 The Blue's Word Boxes

1.	R	O	U	G	H
2.	C	O	U	G	H
3.	C	O	U	C	H
4.	P	O	U	C	H
5.	P	O	A	C	H
6	P	O	R	C	H

Page 153 Secret Scrawls

THE EGGS ARE HIDDEN IN HOG HEAD MOUNTAIN

Pages 154-155 Simply Stella

1. Insecure
2. A bow in her head feathers.
3. She gets angry when she thinks someone is being treated unfairly.
4. Argue or answer back
5. Pink

Page 156 Birdie Kites

Page 158 You Take The Cake

Page 159 Power Cut

A. Chronicler
2. Corporal
C. Foreman
D. King
E. Chef

Page 160–161 Who Am I?

The Mighty Eagle
Sardines
In a remote cave on Piggy Island. Exact location unknown.

Page 162–163 Piggy Island Mash-Up

Creature 1 is Matilda, Foreman Pig and Red
Creature 2 is Hal, Bubbles and Chef Pig

Page 164 Matilda's Mental Maths

509,843
9,738
12,346
50,000,000
600,547

Page 165 Look More Caw-Caw-Fully

30